This book belongs to

Princess AVA

Written by Sue Hunter-Jones
Additional material by Deri Robins
Illustrated by Katie Saunders and Andy Everitt Stewart
Models by Sue Hunter-Jones
Photography by Martin Haswell and Scott Morrison

This is a Parragon Publishing book
This edition published in 2006

Parragon Publishing
Queen Street House
4 Queen Street
Bath BA1 1HE, UK

ISBN 1-40546-094-6
Printed in China

My Princess Craft Book

p

How to use this book

Check the flag at the top of each activity to help you decide what to make…

This activity is quick and easy.

Take more time over this one.

You may need some help.

1. Before you begin, check the **You Will Need** box and gather everything together.

2. Cover your worktop with newspaper in case any paint or glue spills.

3. Read through all the steps before you begin.

4. Follow the steps in order so that you are not waiting for glue or paint to dry.

5. Card templates at the back of the book will help you cut out some of the trickier shapes.

6. If an activity needs glue, use multipurpose school glue. It is easy to use and simple to clean up when it has dried. If you leave the glue to dry for about 30 seconds until it is tacky, it will stick without sliding around.

7. The last section in this book is about food. Remember to wash your hands before you begin.

8. Help clear up when you have finished. Good princesses are always neat!

Make and Play

You will need:

★ toilet paper tube
★ wrapping paper
★ pink tissue paper
★ pink posterboard
★ white paper doily
★ cloth
  (about 8½" x 4¼")
★ strands of knitting yarn
  (about 3" long)
★ ribbon or thread
★ rubber cement
  or glue
★ scissors
★ clear adhesive
  tape

Princess pencil pot

Put your pencils, pens, and treasures into this pretty princess pencil pot.

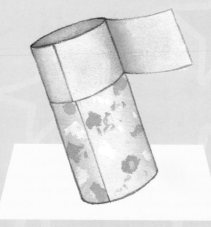

1 Cover the lower two-thirds of the tube with wrapping paper. Cover the top of the tube with pink tissue paper.

2 Cut a strip of paper doily long enough to wrap around the tube. Tape it at the back covering the seam.

3 Glue the cloth about ¾" from the top of the tube. Fold the front edges back and glue down to make a cloak.

4 Cut enough 3" strands of yarn to make the hair. Glue them around the top of the tube. Leave to dry.

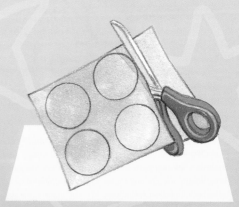

5 Trace around a bottle cap onto pink posterboard. Cut out 4 circles to make hands and feet. Use doily to make sleeves.

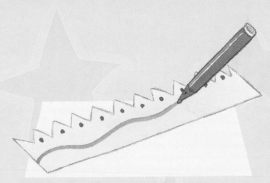

6 Using template 1, cut a crown from a strip of pink posterboard to fit around the tube. Decorate with gold stickers and stars.

7 Glue the crown around the top of the tube. Tape it at the back to hold it in place while it dries.

Tie the wool hair in bunches using thin ribbon or thread.

8 Finally, draw a face to make your princess come to life. Decorate her dress and crown with gold stickers!

Rockinghorse knight

You will need:

★ paper plate
★ poster paint
★ string or knitting yarn (12 strands about 1" long and 5 strands about 2" long)
★ aluminum foil or tissue paper
★ strip of thin cardboard (about 5½" long and ½" wide)
★ toothpick
★ rubber cement or glue
★ scissors
★ clear adhesive tape
★ felt-tip pen

This knight on horseback will rock back and forth just like a real rockinghorse.

1 To make the horse, paint the underneath of the paper plate and leave it to dry.

2 Using template 2, cut a foil cape. Cut some strips of foil for the helmet. Cut a strip of thin cardboard 5½" long and ½" wide.

Keep this piece for the ears and cut them to shape.

Fray one end of each string.

3 Fold the plate in half. Draw around a small cup to make a half-circle. Cut it out. Cut a small piece from the plate to shape the horse's head.

4 Cut a slot in the half-circle to make the knight's helmet. Then, tape strips of foil inside the fold to make a plume for the helmet.

5 Open the plate painted-side down. Tape the long tail string or yarn in place at A, and the short mane string at B.

You can use your gold stickers to make a flag.

6 To make the knight, fold the strip of thin cardboard in half. Glue the folded end inside the helmet. Tape each end to the underside of the plate at X.

7 Using template 11, cut out a flag. Paint one side with glue. Glue it around a toothpick. Tape the flag on the outside of the horse.

8 Glue the cape around the bottom of the helmet. Finally, glue the fringe and ears in place and draw the horse's face.

Pop-up princess

Surprise your friends with a princess who loves to pop up from her castle to say hello!

Use your gold stickers to decorate the castle.

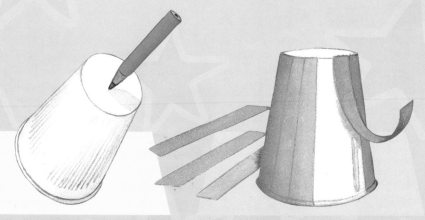

1 Make a hole in the bottom of the cup by gently pressing with the point of a pencil. Don't push too hard or the styrofoam will tear.

2 Cut 12 strips of tissue paper ³⁄₄" wide and the same height as the cup. Cover the cup with glue. Cover it with tissue paper strips. Leave it to dry.

You will need:

★ styrofoam cup

★ sharp pencil

★ tissue paper (12 strips about ³⁄₄" wide)

★ cloth

★ thin posterboard

★ drinking straw

★ scissors

★ lace or net

★ pipe cleaner

★ rubber cement or glue

★ clear adhesive tape

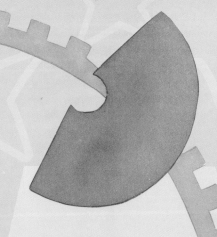

3 Cut a circle of cardboard 1" across and draw the face. Make a crown using two star stickers back to back. Tape the back of the head to a straw.

4 Use template 3 to cut the cloth into shape for the dress. Use template 4 to cut battlements from posterboard.

Use glitter glue to show vines, doors, and windows.

5 Glue around the top of the cup. Lay the cloth right-side down. Roll the edge of the cup along the bottom of the cloth. Leave it to dry.

6 Push the straw down through the hole in the bottom of the cup. Leave about 3/4" poking through at the bottom.

Pinch the cloth to the cup firmly before leaving it to dry.

7 Affix the top of the dress to the straw. Gather the lace or net to make an overdress, and pinch it at the neck.

8 Wrap a pipe cleaner tightly around the net to hold it in place. Twist the pipe cleaner at the back, and straighten out to make the arms.

9 Glue the battlements to the top of the cup and tape them in place while the glue dries. Now you are ready to decorate your castle!

Fairytale castle

If you have dreamed of having a fairytale castle, this one is simple to make!

You will need:

★ 2 paper towel tubes
★ paper towels
★ mailing box
★ heavy string
★ candy wrappers
★ 4 toothpicks
★ colored construction paper
★ posterboard
★ poster paint
★ rubber cement or glue
★ scissors
★ clear adhesive tape
★ glitter

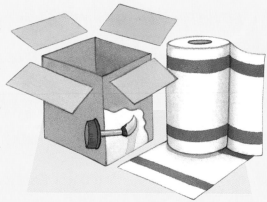

1 Cut the flaps off the top of the box. Paint the box with glue, and cover it with paper towels. Then, paint over the paper towels and leave to dry.

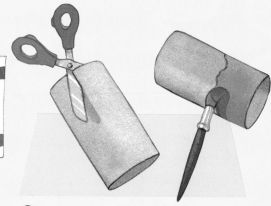

2 Cut the tubes to make 4 towers. Paint them, and leave them to dry.

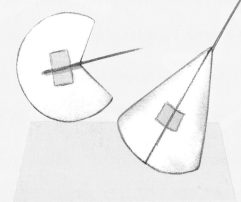

3 Use template 2 to cut 4 cone-shapes out of colored paper. Tape a toothpick in the top to make flagpoles. Roll up the cone and tape together.

12 o'clock

3 o'clock

Cut the slots at 12 o'clock and 3 o'clock

4 When the towers are dry, cut 2 slots from the bottom to about halfway up the tubes.

The four towers can be different heights.

You can use your gold stickers to decorate your castle. Or use colored string, rolled-up wrappers, and glitter.

5 Slot the towers over the corners of the castle. Stick the cones to the top of the towers using small pieces of tape. Add flag stickers to the top of the flagpoles.

6 Use template 5 to cut out 4 long and 4 short battlements. Glue the long battlements around the towers to cover the seams. Glue the short ones to the top of the castle.

Flying dragon puppet

Wiggle this dragon puppet up and down to flap its wings as it flies through the air.

You will need:

- ★ cardboard egg carton
- ★ small mailing box
- ★ poster paint
- ★ posterboard
- ★ paper plate
- ★ string (2 pieces about 8")
- ★ colored tissue paper
- ★ rubber cement or glue
- ★ scissors
- ★ clear adhesive tape
- ★ pipe cleaners
- ★ dowel

1 Cut 4 cups [A] and 5 points [B] from the egg carton. Make a small hole in one cup ready for the string.

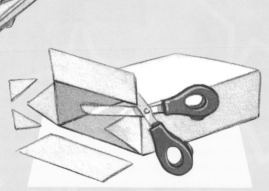

2 To make the head, cut the mailing box in half and cut off the large end flaps. Cut the side flaps into triangles.

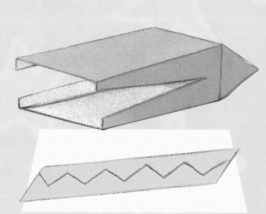

3 Cut a long triangle in each side of the head to shape the mouth. Use template 6 to cut teeth shapes.

4 Paint the cups, points, and head, and leave to dry. Thread string through the cup with the hole, and tie a knot.

5 To make the body, cut a strip of coloured posterboard 1 1/2" wide and 16" long. Glue the head on one end of the body.

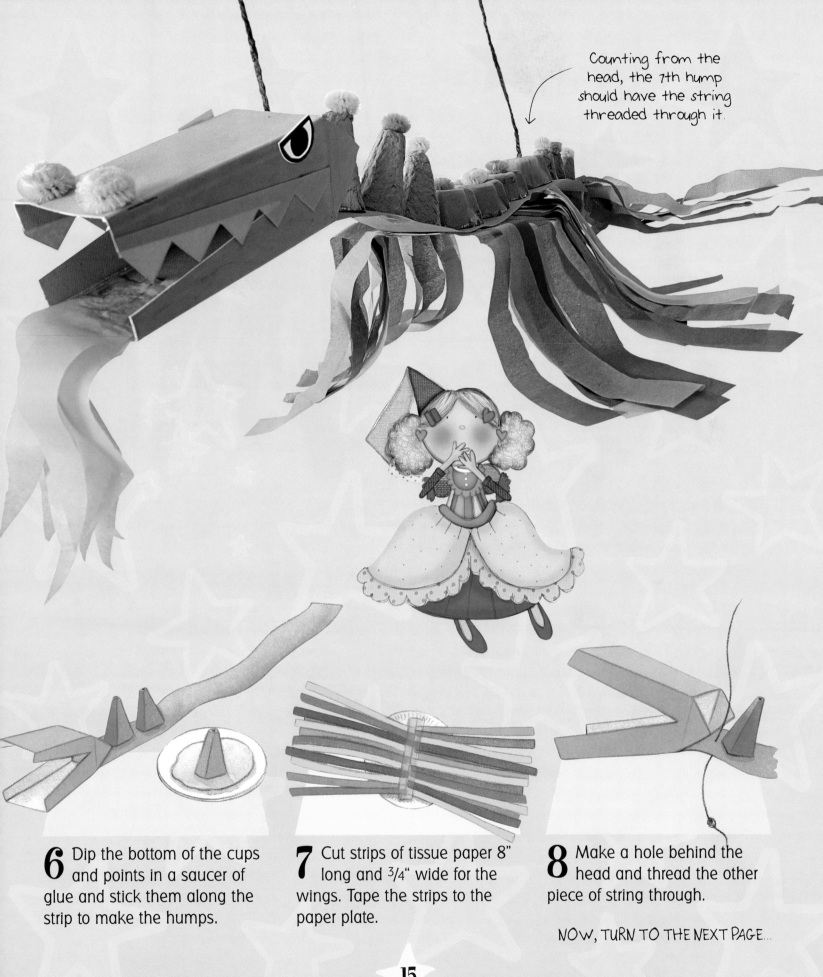

Counting from the head, the 7th hump should have the string threaded through it.

6 Dip the bottom of the cups and points in a saucer of glue and stick them along the strip to make the humps.

7 Cut strips of tissue paper 8" long and 3/4" wide for the wings. Tape the strips to the paper plate.

8 Make a hole behind the head and thread the other piece of string through.

NOW, TURN TO THE NEXT PAGE...

...flying dragon puppet

You can use rolled up tissue paper instead of pipe cleaners.

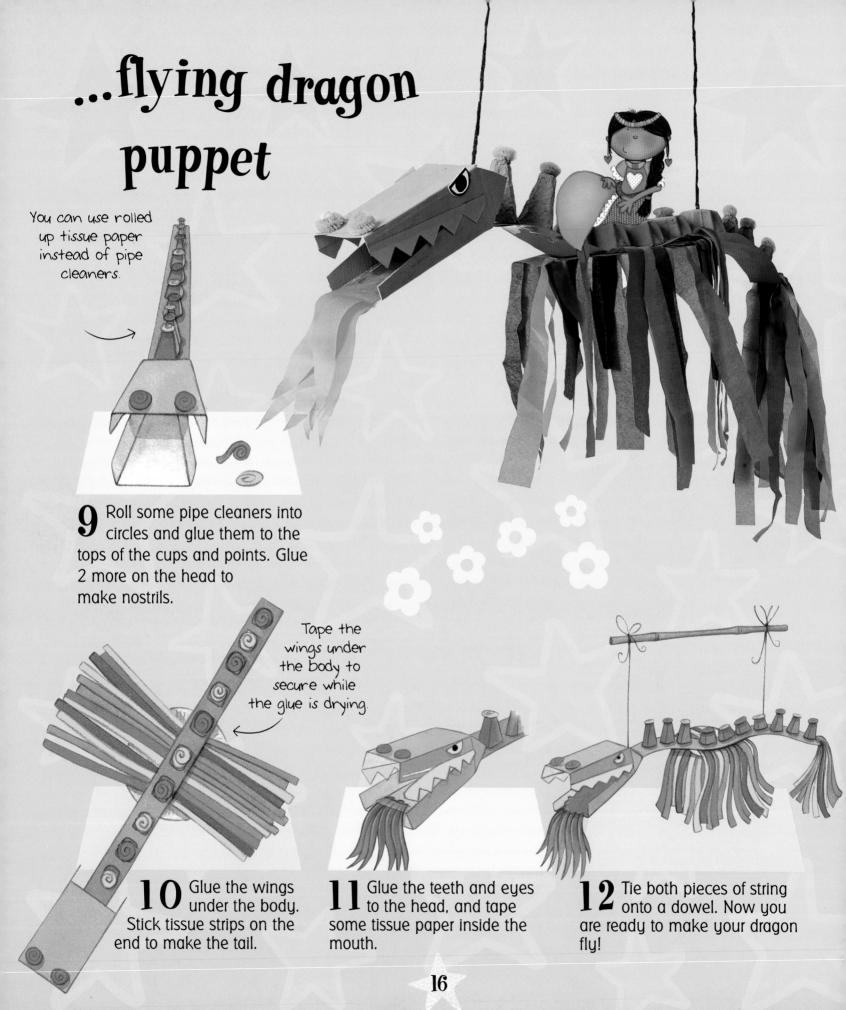

9 Roll some pipe cleaners into circles and glue them to the tops of the cups and points. Glue 2 more on the head to make nostrils.

Tape the wings under the body to secure while the glue is drying.

10 Glue the wings under the body. Stick tissue strips on the end to make the tail.

11 Glue the teeth and eyes to the head, and tape some tissue paper inside the mouth.

12 Tie both pieces of string onto a dowel. Now you are ready to make your dragon fly!

Be a Princess

Pendant necklaces

Make this pretty pendant necklace to wear to the prom. Make one for a friend, too!

You will need:

★ uncooked macaroni
★ lentils
★ poster paints
★ paintbrush
★ newspaper
★ posterboard
★ scissors
★ thin elastic or thread
★ rubber cement or glue
★ gold cord

1 Put about ³/₄" of poster paint into a teacup or saucer. Dip about 25 pieces of pasta halfway into the paint and leave on a newspaper to dry.

2 To make the pendant, use template 7 to cut two shapes out of posterboard, one smaller than the other. Paint them, and leave to dry.

3 When the pasta is dry, dip the unpainted end in another color paint, and leave the pasta beads to dry on a newspaper.

4 When the pendant is dry, glue the smaller shape inside the other shape. Then, glue some lentils on to make a flower decoration.

5 Cut a piece of elastic or thread long enough to fit over your head, leaving room at each end to tie a knot.

Use rolled-up foil or gold stickers to decorate.

6 When the beads are dry, thread them onto your elastic or thread. Try putting different color beads next to each other to make a pattern.

7 When the pendant has dried paint the flower. Make a loop out of gold cord and tape to the back of the pendant.

8 Thread the pendant onto the necklace halfway around. Tie the two ends of elastic together in a knot. Trim off the ends.

Precious purses

This precious purse is perfect for keeping your coins and treasures safe.

You will need:

★ cloth that won't fray or polythene bag

★ 19" cord, ribbon, or yarn

★ 1 large bead

★ large plate and small plate

★ felt-tip pen

★ scissors

★ colored posterboard

★ buttons or beads

Trace onto the wrong side of the cloth so that your marks don't appear on the outside of the purse.

1 Put the cloth face down. Trace around a large plate onto the wrong side of the cloth. Then cut out the circle.

2 Using a smaller plate, draw another circle on to the cloth in the center of the bigger circle.

To make a tiny slit, pinch the cloth together and make a small cut with the scissors.

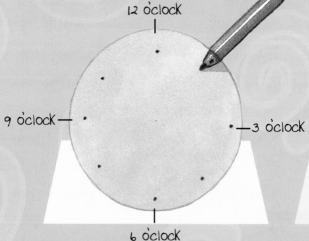

12 o'clock

9 o'clock

3 o'clock

6 o'clock

3 Use a felt tip pen to mark dots at 12, 3, 6, and 9 o'clock around the inner circle. Make dots in between these.

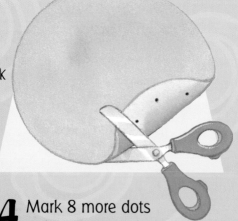

4 Mark 8 more dots in between so that you have 16 dots altogether. Cut a tiny slit on each dot.

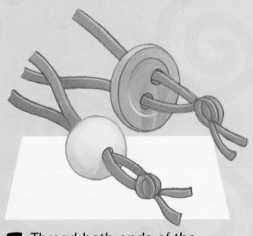

5 Use template 8 to cut a heart shape from colored posterboard. Decorate the card. Make a small hole near the top.

6 Cut a piece of cord, ribbon, or wool long enough to go around the circle twice. Thread it in and out of the slits, slipping the heart on after the 4th slit.

7 Thread both ends of the cord through a large bead or button, and knot the ends together. Now, you are ready to decorate your purse!

You can use *gold stickers* stuck back to back to make a gold tag.

Decorate the purse with *sequins, beads,* or *stick-on jewels.*

Pretty flowers

These pretty flowers tied with ribbon will brighten up any royal palace.

You will need:

★ small saucer
★ plastic drinking straws
★ colored tissue paper
★ pipe cleaner
★ rubber bands
★ clear adhesive tape
★ scissors

1 Draw 5 circles onto tissue paper of different colors, using a small saucer as your template. Cut them out.

2 Fold each circle in half. Then, fold again into quarters. Cut a small piece off the corner to make a hole in the center.

3 Snip about 6 small slots into the top end of a drinking straw. Fold them back to make the center of the flower.

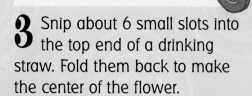

4 Open out the tissue petals. Thread one petal onto the straw, pushing it right to the top of the straw stem. Tape the petal each side to the stem.

To make frilly petals, snip around the edges of the tissue paper

5 Do the same thing with the next 4 petals, mixing the colors and turning the stem each time.

6 Pinch the bottom of the petals to the straw. Then, wind a small rubber band around the straw, and slide it over the petals to hold them in place.

7 Finish your flower by bending a piece of pipe cleaner in half and pushing it into the center of the straw.

Jewelry boxes

Hide away your precious jewels in this gorgeous glittering jewelry box.

You will need:

★ a card-filing box with a lid
★ paint
★ brushes
★ rubber cement or glue
★ aluminum foil
★ paper towels
★ colorful paper

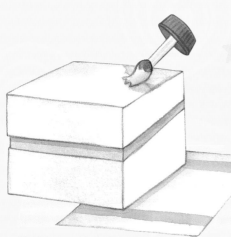

1 Paint the box and lid with glue, and cover with paper towels. Paint it. Leave to dry.

2 Roll up aluminum foil and colorful paper into balls. Glue them to the box and lid.

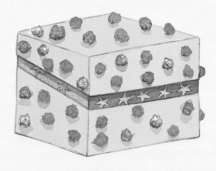

3 Use your gold stickers to decorate the edges.

You will need:

★ a card-filing box with a lid
★ paint
★ flour
★ brushes
★ rubber cement or glue
★ aluminum foil
★ glitter
★ colored tissue paper

1 Mix a little flour into the paint to make it thick, then paint the box and lid. Leave the box to dry.

2 Cut up little squares of aluminum foil. Roll them into long pieces. Then, bend them into spiral shapes.

3 When the box has dried, glue on the foil shapes and decorate with glitter. Put tissue paper inside.

Dazzling tiaras

Every princess needs her own dazzling tiara and matching wand!

You will need

★ posterboard
★ cup
★ rubber cement or glue
★ colored tissue paper
★ curly ribbon
★ pipe cleaners
★ clear adhesive tape
★ scissors

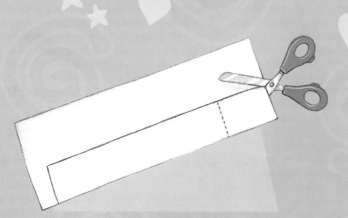

1 Cut a band of posterboard 1" wide and long enough to fit around your head with 1½" overlap at the back. Leave flat.

Tape the string at the back each time until you've done the whole band.

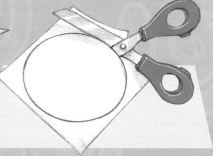

2 Paint the headband with glue, and cover with a layer of tissue paper. Leave it to dry. Then, trim the edges with scissors to make it even.

3 Tape the ribbon to the back of the headband at an angle. Wrap it around the headband and tape it at the other end.

4 Trace a small circle around a cup onto posterboard. Cut it out. Paint it with glue. Cover it with tissue paper, and leave it to dry. Trim the edges.

Here are some ideas for other tiaras you could try making.

5 Tape the circle face down on the center back of the headband so that half the circle shows from the front.

6 Now you are ready to decorate your tiara with gold stickers and rolled-up foil, tissue paper, and glitter.

7 Ask someone to help you hold the band in place around your head, and tape it together at the right size. Then, take it off, and tape the ends.

NOW, TURN TO THE NEXT PAGE...

Matching wands

Decorate your wand to match your tiara.

You will need

★ posterboard
★ dowel
★ aluminum foil
★ rubber cement or glue
★ curly ribbon
★ pipe cleaners
★ clear adhesive tape
★ scissors
★ colored tissue paper

Use two or three pieces of tape to hold it firmly in place.

1 Cut a piece of foil longer than the dowel. Roll it around the stick several times, wrapping it tightly. Twist the ends and fold them back.

2 Use an egg cup to draw a circle onto card. Paint the card with glue, and cover it with tissue paper. Trim the edges to make it even.

3 Tape the shape to the stick. Tie the ribbon around the wand to match your tiara.

Decorate your Palace

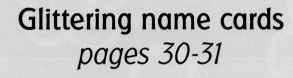

Glittering name cards

Make these name cards for party invitations, place cards, or just for decoration!

You will need:

- ★ cardboard
- ★ posterboard
- ★ poster paint
- ★ string
- ★ paper doily
- ★ aluminum foil
- ★ glitter
- ★ clear adhesive tape

1 Use template 9 to draw a crown shape onto cardboard. Paint it, and leave it to dry. Then, cut it out.

2 Cut a piece of posterboard, and use glitter glue to write your name on it. Decorate with different color dots.

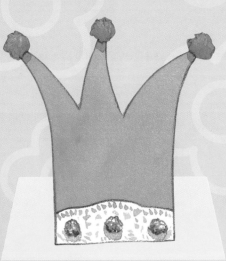

3 Dip some pieces of string in paint and leave them on a newspaper to dry. Roll up aluminum foil to make jewels.

4 Glue the edge of a doily along the bottom of the crown. Dip the jewels in glue, and stick onto the points of the crown and over the doily.

5 Glue your nameplate onto the crown. Measure pieces of string to make a border. Glue them around the nameplate.

Decorate with leftover string, or you can use your gold stickers.

6 To make a door hanger, make a loop of string and tape to the back of the crown.

7 To make a place card, use template 10 to make a stand, and glue it to the back of the crown.

Perfect picture frames

Every princess has her picture on show, so make sure your frame is as pretty as you!

You will need:
★ posterboard
★ poster paint
★ string
★ aluminum foil
★ glitter
★ clear adhesive tape
★ rubber cement or glue
★ scissors

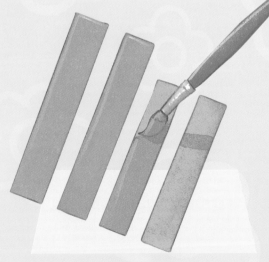

1 Cut out two strips of posterboard 5¹/₂" long and 1" wide. Cut two longer strips 7" long and 1" wide. Paint them, and leave to dry.

2 Use template 10 to cut out a stand from posterboard. Cut a small rectangle of card to make a "stop" so your photo won't fall out of the frame.

3 When the paint is dry, glue the short top and bottom strips over the longer side strips at the corners. Leave to dry.

Decorate your frame with colored shapes or silver foil, or you can use your gold stickers.

You should have a little slot to drop your photo in.

Glue the stop behind.

4 Turn the frame over and glue the "stop"-card at the bottom center of the frame. Leave it to dry.

5 Trace around the outside of your frame onto some posterboard. Cut it out, and glue it to the back of the frame.

6 Fold your card stand and glue it to the back of the frame. The widest part of the stand should be at the bottom.

Shiny suncatcher

You'll never have a gloomy day with this suncatcher twirling overhead.

1 Cut 8 strands of wool of different lengths. The shortest should be about 14". Cut each one 2" longer. Tie a knot in each strand 8" from the end.

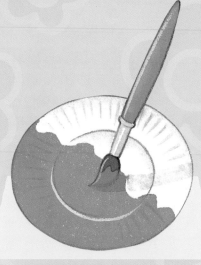

2 Paint both sides of the plate and leave it to dry. Spread a layer of glue over the dry plate to make it shiny. Leave it to dry completely.

You will need:

- ★ paper plate
- ★ poster paint
- ★ yarn
- ★ aluminum foil
- ★ clear colored papers (about 18)
- ★ rubber cement or glue
- ★ scissors

Cut the colored papers in half.

3 Fold the clear colored papers into concertinas. You need 3 for the shortest strands, 4 for the next two, 5 for the next two, and 6 for the two longest strands.

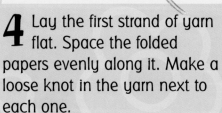

4 Lay the first strand of yarn flat. Space the folded papers evenly along it. Make a loose knot in the yarn next to each one.

5 Thread the paper through, and tighten the knot. Tie a second knot to secure it. Pull the ends open in a fan to look like a butterfly. Do this on all 8 strands.

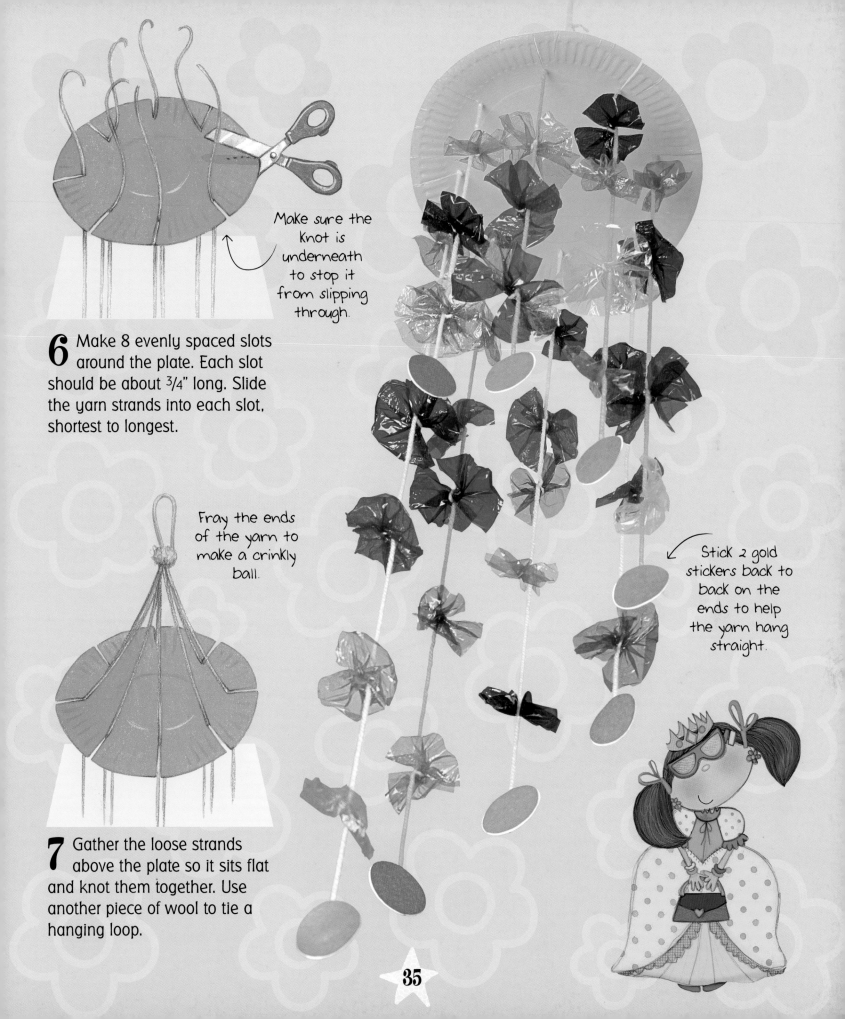

Make sure the knot is underneath to stop it from slipping through.

6 Make 8 evenly spaced slots around the plate. Each slot should be about 3/4" long. Slide the yarn strands into each slot, shortest to longest.

Fray the ends of the yarn to make a crinkly ball.

Stick 2 gold stickers back to back on the ends to help the yarn hang straight.

7 Gather the loose strands above the plate so it sits flat and knot them together. Use another piece of wool to tie a hanging loop.

Fabulous fortuneteller

Your friends will be lining up to choose their futures on your fabulous fortuneteller.

You will need:

★ a square of paper
★ felt tip pens
★ scissors

1 To make a square of paper, fold the paper from one corner, bringing the short edge to meet the long edge. Cut off the extra paper.

2 To find the center, fold the paper corner to corner to make a triangle. Open it out flat. Now fold the opposite corners together.

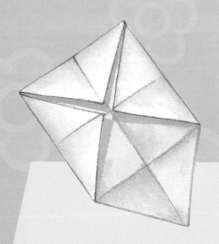

3 Open it flat again. Next, fold all four corners into the center.

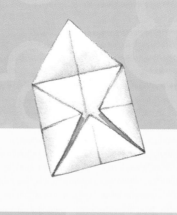

4 Turn it over and fold all four corners into the middle again.

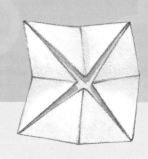

5 Fold it in half to make a crease. Open it out. Fold it in half the other way to make another crease.

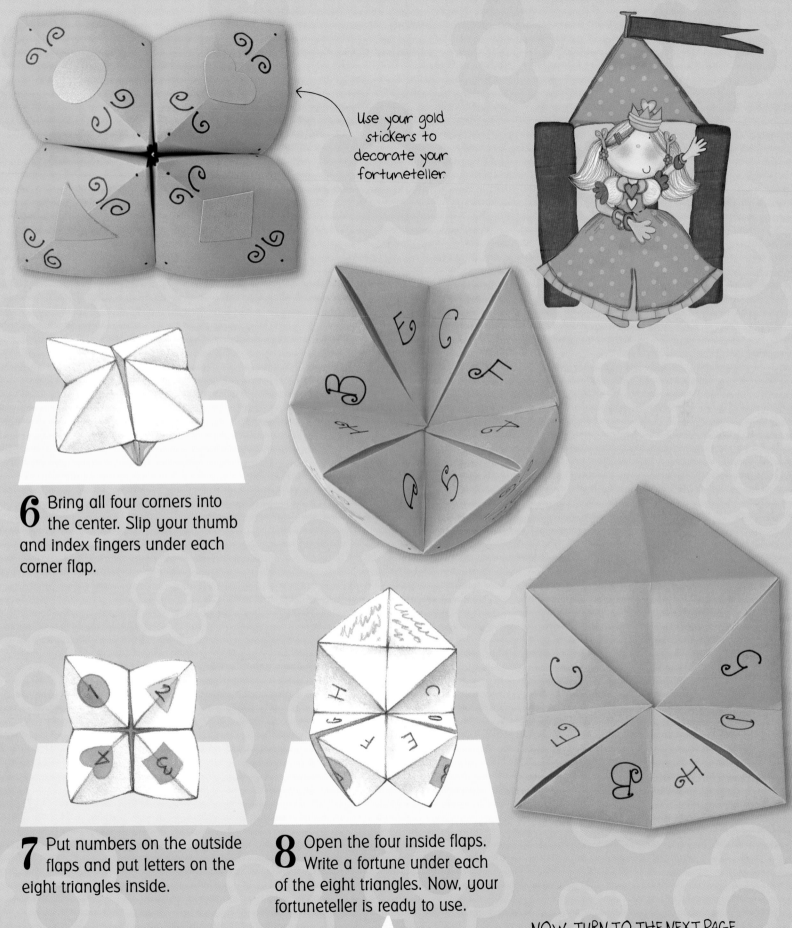

Use your gold stickers to decorate your fortuneteller.

6 Bring all four corners into the center. Slip your thumb and index fingers under each corner flap.

7 Put numbers on the outside flaps and put letters on the eight triangles inside.

8 Open the four inside flaps. Write a fortune under each of the eight triangles. Now, your fortuneteller is ready to use.

NOW, TURN TO THE NEXT PAGE...

How to tell your fortune

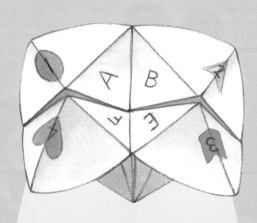

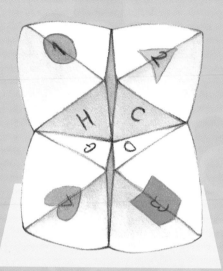

1 To use the fortuneteller, pinch your index fingers and thumbs together, opening the fortuneteller left to right.

2 Then press your index fingers together and your thumbs together, opening the fortuneteller forward and back.

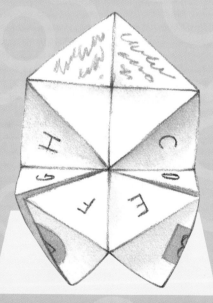

3 Ask a friend to choose a number from the outside of your fortuneteller. Open and close the fortuneteller that number of times.

4 When you have stopped, ask them to choose a letter from one of the four inside flaps. Open the flap to read their fortune!

Here are some fortunes to write inside your fortuneteller:

You will grow your hair down to your toes.

All your dreams will come true.

You will live in a fairytale castle.

You will dance with a Prince.

You will have a magic wand.

You will kiss a frog!

You will escape from a wicked witch.

You will have a pet unicorn called Sparkle.

Make a Feast

Queen of hearts sandwiches
pages 40-41

Fancy fridge cake
pages 42-43

Delicious drinks
pages 44-45

How to decorate your feast
page 46

Queen of hearts sandwiches

Here are some suggestions for tasty sandwiches
—or make up your own fillings!

You will need:

(makes enough for
8 heart sandwiches)

★ sliced bread

★ butter

★ raspberry or
strawberry jam or a
sandwich filling of
your choice

★ knife

1 Wash your hands and put on an apron. Take 8 slices of bread and butter each slice on one side.

2 Cut off the crusts. You could save these to put on a bird table or to feed ducks!

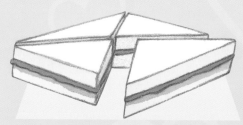

3 Spread 2 slices of bread with jam. Put two buttered slices on top, butter-side down. Cut the sandwiches from corner to corner to make 4 triangles.

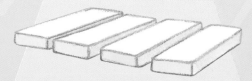

4 Cut each of the remaining slices of bread into 4 long fingers. You should have 16 fingers altogether.

You can use your gold stickers to make sandwich flags.

5 Spread the fingers with jam. Don't put too much jam on, or it will squish out when you roll them up.

6 Roll up each finger into a mini roll. Cut each roll into four to make thick spirals.

7 Arrange the spirals and the triangles on the plate to make heart shapes.

TO MAKE SOME SANDWICH FLAGS, TURN TO PAGE 46.

Fancy fridge cake

You'll need some friends to share this delicious cake with.

You will need:

(makes enough for 16)

★ 5oz plain chocolate
★ 8oz granola
★ 1oz butter
★ 3 tablespoons molasses
★ 16 candy decorations
★ 7-inch square cake pan
★ mixing bowl
★ wooden spoon
★ saucepan
★ knife

1 Wash your hands and put on an apron. Gather together a mixing bowl, wooden spoon, and cake pan. Carefully measure out the chocolate, granola, butter, and molasses.

2 Grease the cake pan using some butter or margarine. This will make the cake come out of the pan more easily.

Ask a grownup to help with heating the saucepan.

3 Break the chocolate into chunks, and put them in a saucepan. Add the molasses and butter. Melt over low heat, stirring constantly.

4 Stir in the granola. Then pour the mixture into the cake pan. Arrange your candy decorations in rows on top of the cake.

5 Put the cake pan in the refrigerator and leave it for 2 hours until set solid.

6 Cut the cake into squares, and arrange in a pattern on the plate.

Delicious drinks

Try this Super Smoothie or a Fruity Milkshake. They're fun to make and drink!

Super Smoothie

You will need:
(makes enough for 4)

★ 1 small banana
★ 1 ripe pear
★ ½ cup apple juice
★ ½ small carton of plain yogurt
★ 1 tablespoon honey
★ measuring cup
★ cutting board
★ knife
★ blender

Ask a grownup to help with chopping the pear.

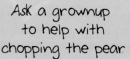

1 Wash your hands and put on an apron. Slice a banana into chunks. Peel and chop a pear. Take out the core and seeds.

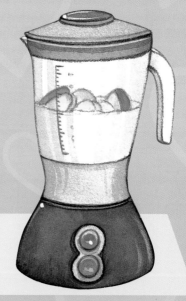

2 Put the fruit, yogurt, and apple juice in the blender. Close the lid, and blend until smooth.

3 Taste first, and add honey if it tastes too sharp. Pour your Super Smoothie into glasses.

TO MAKE YOUR SWIZZLESTICKS, TURN TO PAGE 46.

Fruity Milkshake

You will need:

(makes enough for 4)

★ 1 small banana
★ 8 strawberries or 12 raspberries
★ 1 cup of milk
★ sugar to taste
★ measuring cup
★ cutting board
★ knife
★ blender

Make sure the lid is on tight before you start the blender!

Remove the green leaves.

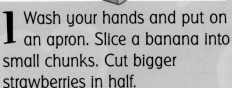

1 Wash your hands and put on an apron. Slice a banana into small chunks. Cut bigger strawberries in half.

2 Put the fruit into a blender. Pour in the milk. Close the lid, and blend until smooth.

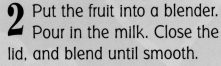

3 Taste first, and add sugar if it tastes too sharp. Pour your Fruity Milkshake into glasses.

TO DECORATE YOUR DRINKING STRAW, TURN TO PAGE 46.

How to decorate your feast

1 To make sandwich flags, use template 11 to cut out some flag shapes.

2 Put a toothpick in the center. Then, fold the flag shape over and glue.

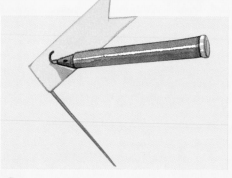

3 Use a pen to write the sandwich filling on the flag. Then, spear it into the top sandwich on the plate.

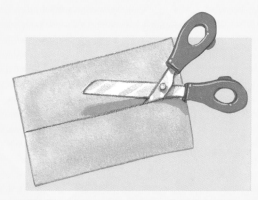

1 To decorate a drinking straw, cut a strip of colored paper about 2" long, and 3/4" wide.

2 Cut about halfway across and along the whole length to make a fringe.

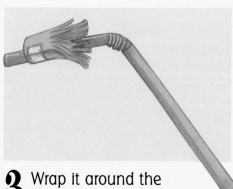

3 Wrap it around the drinking straw and tape it in position.

1 To make swizzlesticks, chop bananas, strawberries, and grapes.

2 Push the fruit chunks onto a toothpick.

3 You can add pineapple chunks and candied cherries.

Templates